Christmas STORY

THE Christmas STORY

Abridged by Joyce McAleer
Illustrated by Amanda Hall

THE CHRISTMAS STORY

AN ANGEL VISITS

Although Jesus spent his early life much like other boys, his birth was very special and unusual. We call the events surrounding his birth the Nativity and we remember them every year at Christmas. This is the story of what happened.

Jesus' mother was called Mary and she lived in a town called Nazareth. She was engaged to be married to Joseph who was a local carpenter. Although she didn't realise it at the beginning, Mary was no ordinary girl, in fact she was very special indeed. She had been chosen by God to be the mother of his son, Jesus. Mary learnt her important role in a very unusual way. God sent an angel to speak to her and tell her the good news. This angel was called Gabriel and appeared to Mary saying, "Don't be afraid, Mary. God has chosen you to be the mother of his son. His name will be 'Jesus' and he will be a king whose reign will never end."

But Mary was puzzled and confused. She said to the angel, "I am a virgin. How, then, can this be?" Gabriel replied, "With God nothing is impossible. The Holy Spirit will come to you and God's power will rest upon you. For this reason the holy child will be called the Son of God."

Gabriel went on to give Mary some more

incredible news. He said that her cousin, Elizabeth, would also have a child, which would be born in a few months time. Mary was amazed to hear this because Elizabeth was very old and had never had children before. But Mary never doubted what Gabriel said, she told him, "I am God's servant, may it happen as you have said."

MARY VISITS ELIZABETH

Some time later, Mary decided to go and visit her cousin, Elizabeth, to talk about the babies they were both expecting.

As Mary entered the house, she called out a friendly greeting. The moment Elizabeth heard Mary's voice, she felt her baby move. Elizabeth was filled with the Holy Spirit and cried out to Mary, "You are blessed among women, and blessed be the child you will have! I am so fortunate to have my Lord's mother actually visit me. As soon as I heard your voice, my baby leaped within me with sheer joy."

Mary was pleased that Elizabeth shared her wonderful secret and joyfully thanked God for all that had happened.

Mary stayed with Elizabeth until her baby was born and, sure enough, it was a boy just as the angel had foretold.

When the baby was a few days old, he was named John. He grew up to be known as John the Baptist and became a great prophet, telling people about Jesus and urging them to follow him.

JOSEPH'S DREAM

Although Joseph was a good and kind man, when he found out that Mary was pregnant, he was troubled and unsure what to do. But one night an angel appeared to him in a dream, saying, "Joseph, do not be worried or afraid about marrying Mary, because the child she is carrying is the child of the Holy Spirit. She will have a son, who will be called Jesus. He will save his people from their sins."

Joseph woke up feeling much better. His mind was now at rest and he understood that Mary, his future bride, was special and why such an extraordinary thing had happened to her. The next morning he hurried to see her. "Mary," he said, "I realise now that God has chosen me to take care of you and your son. An angel came to me in a dream and told me that you are to be the mother of the Lord."

THE EMPEROR'S ORDERS

Mary and Joseph got married and moved into Joseph's house beside the carpenter shop. But one day Joseph came home with some bad news. The Emperor of Rome, Augustus, had ordered everyone to travel to whichever town or city they came from in order to register themselves to be taxed.

Joseph was descended from King David, so he had to travel to the city of David. This was a place called Bethlehem.

Mary, who was nearly ready to have her baby, went with him. As there was no other way to travel, they rode on a donkey. The journey was long and tiring and by the time they arrived in Bethlehem Mary and Joseph were feeling exhausted.

The town was absolutely packed with other people who had also come to be taxed. The streets were noisy and full of families and their animals. Joseph asked at the inn for a place to stay but, like the rest of the city, it was full. Desperately he asked it there was anywhere at all where they could rest. He was very worried about Mary, who was due to have her baby at any time.

Finally the innkeeper suggested the stable where he kept his animals. Reluctantly Joseph agreed, at least it would provide them with shelter for the night.

JESUS IS BORN!

Unfortunately no rooms became free at the inn and Mary and Joseph stayed in the stable with the animals for several days. One night Mary realised the time had come for the baby to be born. There was nothing she could do, nowhere she could go for help – so Jesus was born right there, in the stable, surrounded by animals.

Mary and Joseph gazed in wonder at the tiny baby. Mary recalled in her heart the words of the angel Gabriel, and Joseph thought of the angel who had appeared to him in the dream. They realised that they were looking at the son of God.

Mary wrapped her cherished baby in strips of cloth and put him in a manger – a feeding trough used by the animals. This is how Jesus started his life, humbly amongst the animals in a stable.

SHEPHERDS HEAR THE NEWS

That same night some shepherds were watching their sheep on the hills outside the city. Suddenly a great light shone over them and an angel appeared in the sky above them. The shepherds were very startled and trembled with fear, but the angel said, "Don't be afraid! I am here with good news for you, which will bring great joy to all the people. This very day in the city of David, your Saviour was born – Christ the Lord!" The shepherds listened in amazement as the angel continued, "You can find out for yourselves. The baby is wrapped in strips of cloth and lying in a manger."

Then, suddenly, the sky was filled with a great choir of angels, who all cried out in praise of God, "Glory to God in the highest and on earth, peace and goodwill towards men."

Then the angels left the shepherds, the beautiful light disappeared and once again it was dark and still on the Bethlehem hills. The shepherds, still

overwhelmed by their experience, turned to one another and talked about what it all meant. One of them said boldy, "The angel said we would find the Saviour in a manger, let's go to Bethlehem and see him." The others agreed, although they could scarcely believe what they had seen, and they were amazed that God has sent his angel to tell them – just poor shepherds. They hurried eagerly towards the city.

As they entered the gates of Bethlehem, they turned towards the inn and noticed a light in the stable. Inside the stable they found Mary and Joseph and, just as the angel had told them, a baby wrapped in strips of cloth was lying in a manger. They marvelled at this, and repeated the angel's words to Mary and Joseph. Mary listened carefully to the words the shepherds spoke and thought about them deeply. The shepherds looked at the baby and praised God for the wonderful thing that had happened. Then they turned and quietly went away.

A STAR IN THE EAST

At the same time, far away in an eastern land, three wise men were standing, gazing in wonder at a star in the sky. This star was much larger and brighter than any other. They knew at once that it was a sign from God that the promised Messiah had come.

They followed the star as it moved

through the sky, for many months. They asked everyone they met, "Where is the child born to be King of the Jews? We saw his star rise in the east and we have come to worship him." Nobody knew what they were talking about, they replied, "You must be mistaken, no king has been born here recently."

Eventually the wise men followed the star to Bethlehem, where it stopped above the house where Jesus was. As they entered the house they saw the baby Jesus and knelt in front of him and worshipped him. Then they offered precious gifts to the child; gold, frankincense and myrrh.

On their way to Bethlehem, the three wise men had visited King Herod who had been told by priests that a child would be born in Bethlehem who would become king of the Jews.

Herod asked the wise men to come back to his palace after they had worshipped Jesus, to tell him where the child lay. He pretended that he, too, wanted to worship the baby, but in fact he was so jealous of the child, that he was determined to kill him.

The night before the three wise men set off to return to Herod's palace, they each had the same dream – that Herod was planning to kill Jesus, so they decided to go home by a different route.

Back in his palace, Herod became angrier and angrier and when it became obvious that the wise men were not coming to him, the furious king decided to kill every baby in Bethlehem!

But before he could do this, an angel visited Joseph and told him what Herod planned to do. Joseph immediately told Mary to get ready for a journey and in the middle of the night, he led his wife and baby out of the town.

They journeyed for many days until they came to Egypt where they stayed until an angel told Joseph that Herod was dead and it was safe to return to Nazareth.

This is the end of the story of the first Christmas, but it is only the beginning of the wonderful life of Jesus. It is hard to imagine that the little baby lying in a stable, surrounded by animals, was sent by God to help and save us all. But as he grew older, by his teachings and by the way he lived, Jesus taught us the best way to lead our lives. His life, words and miracles were all written down by Jesus' followers and we can read about them in The Bible.

First published in this abridged version by Carnival in 1988.

Carnival is an imprint of
the Children's Division, part of
the Collins Publishing Group,
8 Grafton Street, London W1X 3LA

Published by Carnival 1988
Reprinted 1989

ISBN 0 00 194549 1

Printed and bound in Great Britain by
PURNELL BOOK PRODUCTION LIMITED
A Member of BPCC plc